CW00972044

Read about Greenbug's adventures when he takes to the air in his small plane. Show-off Rudolf Von Flugel flies his plane upside-down, Lindy Pig makes a parachute jump, Lowly Worm flies in his apple plane – and lots more! Don't forget to help Greenbug look for his friend Goldbug.

Richard Scarry's

Planes

Published in Great Britain with the authorization
of Winthers Forlag A/S by
World International Publishing Ltd., an Egmont Company,
Egmont House, PO Box 111, Great Ducie Street,
Manchester M60 3BL.
Printed in Germany. ISBN 0-7498-0428-9
REPRINTED 1992

Greenbug has a small plane.
Everywhere he goes, he looks for his friend, Goldbug.

Hello! I'm Goldbug.

Can you find Goldbug in
each picture?

Huckle Cat and Lowly Worm have a plane with two sets of wings. It's called a biplane.

Greenbug's plane has one wing
on each side.

This plane has three wings.

Rudolf Von Flugel likes to fly
his plane upside-down.
He's a bit of a show-off.

VRRRROOOOM!
Two jet planes flash by.

Where is Goldbug?

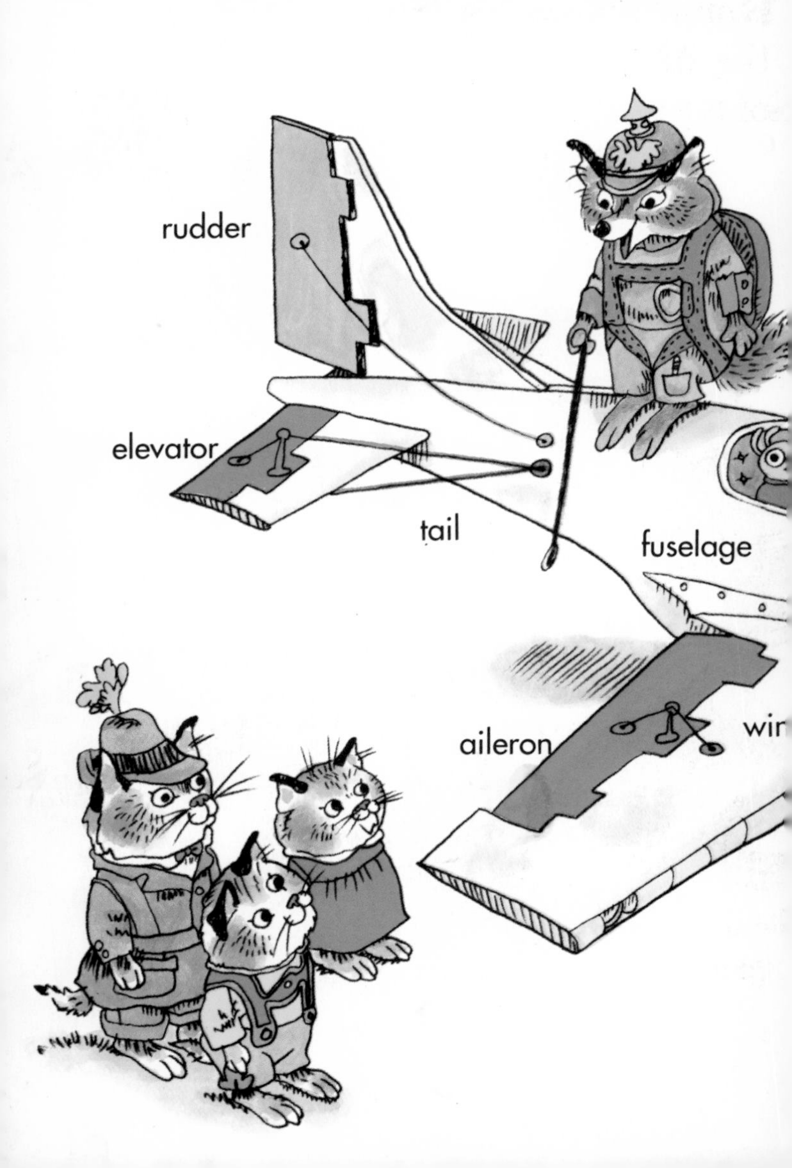
rudder
elevator
tail
fuselage
aileron
wir

Rudolf shows his friends
the different parts
of a plane.

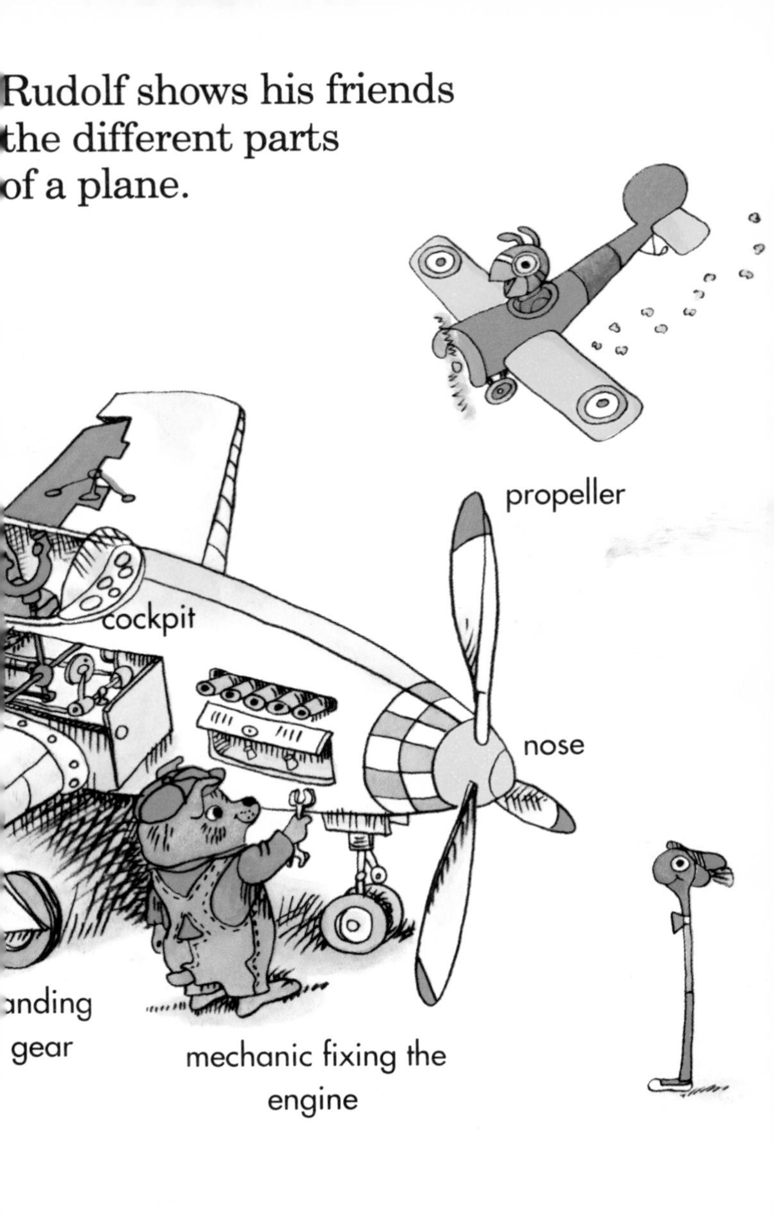

Keep your planes away from the windmill!
It is bigger than you, and very dangerous.

Watch out, Greenbug!

Balloons and kites fly in the air.
Don't let your balloon fly away.

Here are some old planes.

Look out, Greenbug!
That plane might eat you!

Lindy Pig jumps from a plane.
He wears a parachute.
He floats down to the ground.

A blimp is big and sausage-shaped.
It is filled with gas.
It floats in the air.

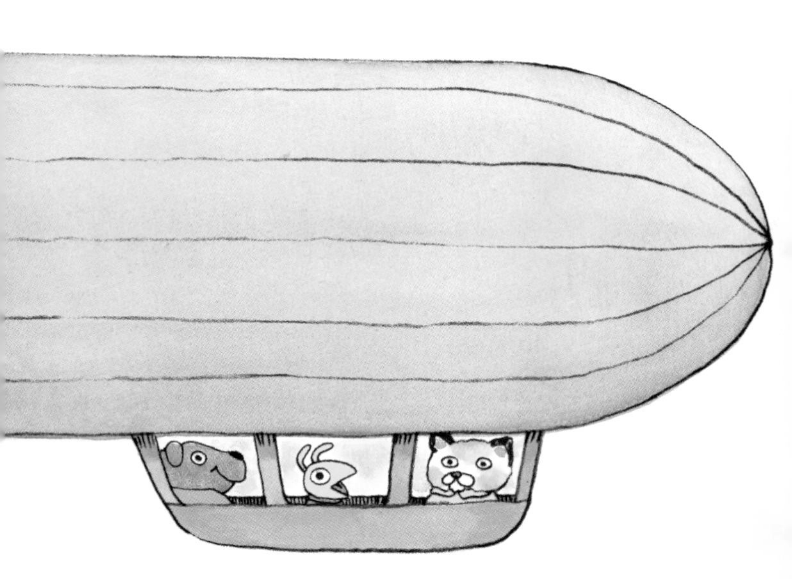

What is Greenbug doing?
He is flying downwards!

Helicopters fly up and down, as well as forwards and backwards.
Maybe Greenbug thinks he flies a helicopter.

Lowly Worm has an apple plane!

Greenbug is going to land his plane.

The jet is getting ready for take-off.

Greenbug lands his plane.
But he doesn't do it very well. Look!
Mr Fixit mends it for him.

"Are you okay,
Greenbug?"
"Yes, thank you."